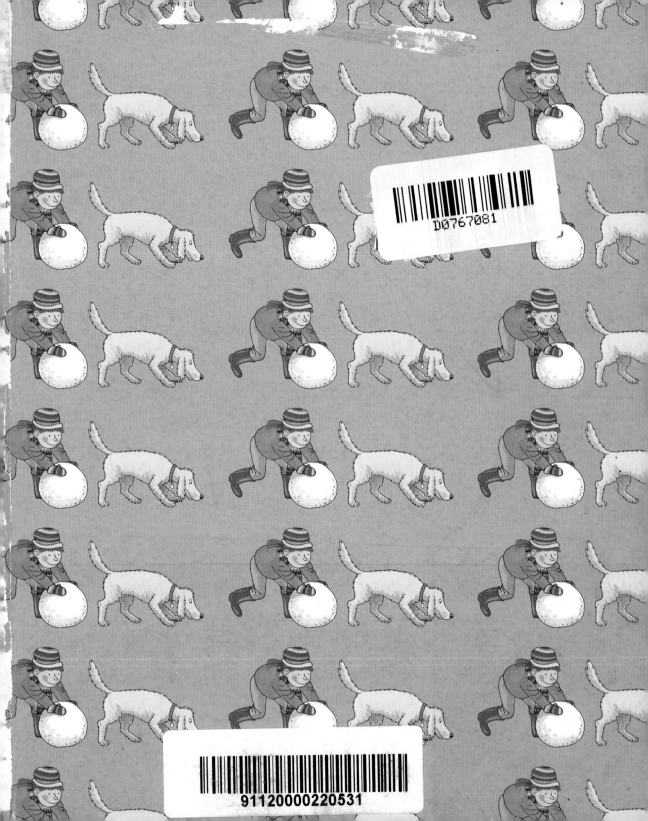

This book belongs to ...

....

OXFORD
UNIVERSITY PRESS

Great Clarendon Street, Oxford, OX2 6DP,
United Kingdom

Oxford University Press is a department of the University of Oxford.
It furthers the University's objective of excellence in research, scholarship,
and education by publishing worldwide. Oxford is a registered trade mark of
Oxford University Press in the UK and in certain other countries

Egg Fried Rice, Dolphin Rescue, Husky Adventure text © Roderick Hunt 2005, 2008
Trapped! text © Cynthia Rider 2006
Trapped!, Husky Adventure illustrations © Alex Brychta 2005, 2006
Egg Fried Rice, Dolphin Rescue illustrations © Alex Brychta and Nick Schon 2008

The characters in this work are the original creation of Roderick Hunt
and Alex Brychta who retain copyright in the characters.

The moral rights of the author have been asserted
Husky Adventure first published in 2005
Trapped! first published in 2006
Egg Fried Rice, Dolphin Rescue first published in 2008
This Edition published in 2013

ISBN: 978-0-19-273435-8

3 5 7 9 10 8 6 4 2

Typeset in Edbaskerville

Paper used in the production of this book is a natural, recyclable product made
from wood grown in sustainable forests. The manufacturing process conforms
to the environmental regulations of the country of origin.

Acknowledgements;
Series Editors: Kate Ruttle, Annemarie Young

READ WITH
Biff,
Chip &
Kipper

Husky Adventure
and Other Stories

Egg Fried Rice 6

Dolphin Rescue 36

Trapped! 66

Husky Adventure 96

OXFORD
UNIVERSITY PRESS

Tips for Reading Together

Children learn best when reading is fun.

- Talk about the title and the picture on the front cover.

- Identify the letter patterns *ie, igh, i-e* and *y* in the story, and talk about the sound they make when you read them ('igh').

- Look at the *ie, i-e, igh,* and *y* words on page 4. Say the sounds in each word and then say the word (e.g. *f-r-ie-d, fried; r-i-ce, rice; l-igh-t, light; t-r-y, try*).

- Read the story then find the words with *ie* and *i-e, igh* and *y*.

- Talk about the story and do the fun activity at the end of the book.

Children enjoy re-reading stories and this helps to build their confidence.

After you have read the story, see how many chinese lanterns you can find.

The main sound practised in this book is 'igh' as in *tried, nine, night,* and *cried.*

For more hints and tips on helping your child become a successful and enthusiatic reader look at our website www.oxfordowl.co.uk.

Egg Fried Rice

Written by Roderick Hunt
Illustrated by Nick Schon,
based on the original characters
created by Roderick Hunt and Alex Brychta

OXFORD
UNIVERSITY PRESS

Say the sound and read the words

igh

br**igh**t

l**igh**t

r**igh**t

ie

fr**ie**d

tr**ie**d

cr**ie**d

8

y

try

sky

cry

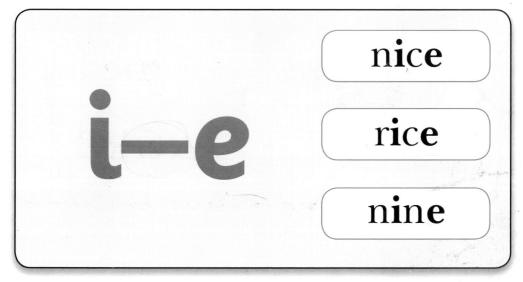

i–e

nice

rice

nine

9

"I will be nine on Friday," said
Wilma. "I'd like to eat out."

"I'd like a Chinese meal," Wilma said,
"and can we invite Biff and Chip?"

"That's fine," said Mum.

It was time for the Chinese meal.

They went to the Bright Sky.

"What is it like to be nine?" said Chip.

Wilma smiled.

"It's all right," she said.

"What do you like best?"
said Dad.

"I like egg fried rice," said Wilma,
"and I'll try tiger prawns."

17

Then all the lights went out.

Oh no! There was a fire.

"The kitchen is on fire!" said
Mr Lee.

They had to go outside.
Fire-fighters came to put the
fire out.

"I am sorry," said Mr Lee.

"We must shut for the night."

Wilma was upset. She tried not to, but she cried.

"It is sad to see Wilma cry," said
Mr Lee. "Come back on Sunday night."

On Sunday, Mr Lee put on
a feast.

"Smile," said Mr Lee.

"This is so kind," said Mum.

"I had my egg fried rice," said
Wilma, "and such a nice time."

Talk about the story

Where did
the family go
for their meal?

Why did the
family go out
for a meal?

What did
Wilma like
to eat?

29

Word jumble

Make the *igh*, *ie*, *i–e* and *y* words from the story.

t r igh b

n e f i

s igh l t

y r c

e n c i

30

k s y

ie f d r

i c r e

c ie r d

Happy
Birthday
Wilma

31

Picture puzzle

Find as many *igh*,
ie, *i–e* and *y* words as
you can in the picture.

y

ie

igh

i-e

ie, i-e, y or igh?

Choose the letters to make each word.

n____t   n__n__   sm__l__

tr____d   l__k__   r____t

br____t   fr____d   cr__

Tips for Reading Together

Children learn best when reading is fun.

- Talk about the title and the picture on the front cover.
- Identify the letter pattern *ph* in the title and talk about the sound it makes when you read it ('f').
- Look at the *ph* words on page 4. Say the sounds in each word and then say the word (e.g. *d-o-l-ph-i-n*, *dolphin*).
- Read the story then find the words with *ph*.
- Talk about the story and do the fun activity at the end of the book.

Children enjoy re-reading stories and this helps to build their confidence.

After you have read the story, find eight starfish hidden in the pictures.

The main sound practised in this book is 'f' as in *fin* and *dolphin*. The other sound practised is 'ee' as in *beach* and *deep*.

For more hints and tips on helping your child become a successful and enthusiastic reader look at our website www.oxfordowl.co.uk.

Dolphin Rescue

Written by Roderick Hunt
Illustrated by Nick Schon,
based on the original characters
created by Roderick Hunt and Alex Brychta

OXFORD
UNIVERSITY PRESS

37

Say the sound and read the words

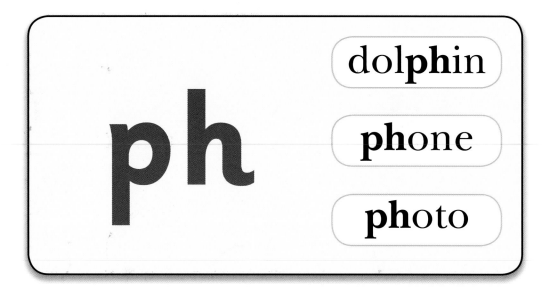

dolphin

phone

photo

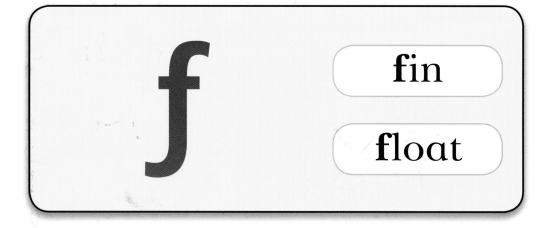

fin

float

ee

deep

need

keep

ea

beach

team

sea

leave

A grey shape lay on the beach.

"Oh no!" said Gran. "It's a dolphin."
"Why is it lying there?" said Wilf.

"It has lost its way," said Gran.
"It needs to go back into deep water."

Some men got to the dolphin.

"Let's pull it back in the sea," said a man.

Gran ran up to the men.

"No!" she cried. "Leave it alone."

"I will phone the dolphin rescue team," she said. "They will get it back into deep water."

Gran told Wilma to keep all the
children away.

"It is lying on its side," said Gran.
"Get it upright."

Dig holes for its fins.

"Keep it cool," said Gran.

"It needs shade."

Get buckets
of water.

"Don't get water in the
blow-hole," said a man.

A man tried to take a photo of
the dolphin.

Soon the dolphin rescue team came.

The rescue team put the dolphin on
a float.

The rescue team took the dolphin
back into the sea.

"I hope the dolphin will be all right,"
said Biff.

Talk about the story

Why was the dolphin on the sand?

What did the men want to do?

Why did Gran phone the dolphin rescue team?

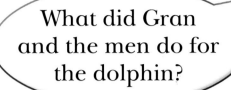

What did Gran
and the men do for
the dolphin?

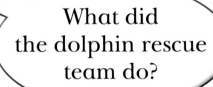

What did
the dolphin rescue
team do?

Have you
helped a creature in
distress? How?

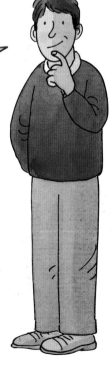

59

Word jumble

Make the *f* and *ph* words and the *ee* and *ea* words from the story.

ee	s	

i	f	n

p	k	ee

m	ea	t

n	d	ee	s

ph   i   o   l   d   n

ea   ch   b

ee   d   p

61

f or ph?

The sound 'f' can be spelled *f* and *ph*. Match the right 'f' spelling to the pictures and complete the word.

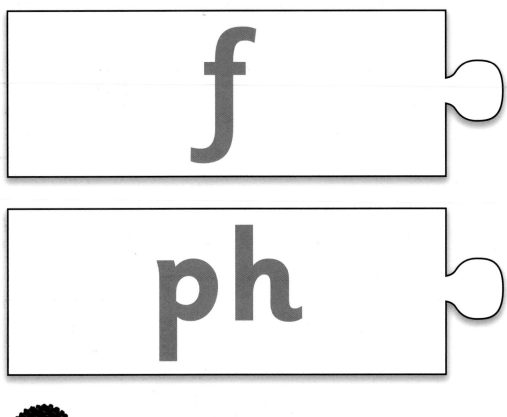

dol__in

_ish

__one

_loppy

ele__ant

A maze

Help the dolphin find its way out to the open sea.

Tips for Reading Together

Children learn best when reading is fun.

- Talk about the title and the picture on the front cover.

- Discuss what you think the story might be about.

- Read the story together, inviting your child to read as much of it as they can.

- Give lots of praise as your child reads, and help them when necessary.

- If they get stuck, try reading the first sound of the word, or break the word into chunks, or read the whole sentence again. Focus on the meaning.

- Re-read the story later, encouraging your child to read as much of it as they can.

Children enjoy re-reading stories and this helps to build their confidence.

Have fun!

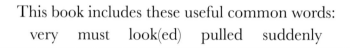

After you have read the story, find the 7 hidden keys, and the letters and letter shapes that make up the word TRAPPED.

This book includes these useful common words:
very   must   look(ed)   pulled   suddenly

For more hints and tips on helping your child become a successful and enthusiastic reader look at our website www.oxfordowl.co.uk.

Trapped!

Written by Cynthia Rider
based on the original characters
created by Roderick Hunt and Alex Brychta
Illustrated by Alex Brychta

OXFORD
UNIVERSITY PRESS

Please return
the key

Keep dogs
on a lead

Gran took the children and
Floppy to see an old castle.

The children went up the path to
the castle. Suddenly, Chip stopped.

He pointed to a window at the top.
"Look, there's a face," he said.

Everyone looked, but the face
had gone.

"It can't be a face," said Gran.

"The castle is empty."

They went into the castle.

"It looks very old," said Biff.

"And very scary!" said Kipper.

"Let's play hide and seek," said
Chip.

The children ran in and out of
the rooms.

"I'll play too," said Gran, and
she went into the next room.

Gran looked for a place to hide.
She saw a gate and pulled it open.

CLANG! The gate banged shut.

Gran pushed it, but it was stuck.

"Help! Help!" she shouted.

The children ran to see what had happened.

"I'm trapped," said Gran.

The gate was very stiff.
The children pulled and pulled.
At last, it opened.

"I'll keep the gate open with this old chest," said Gran. "I don't want to be trapped again."

"Come on," said Kipper. "Let's see
where these stairs go."

They all went up the stairs.

Suddenly, they heard a noise.
Woo...ooo! WOO...OOO!
"What was that?" said Biff.

The noise came again.

Woo...ooo! WOO...OOO!

Floppy pulled at his lead and raced up the stairs.

"Come on! We must go after
Floppy," said Chip. They all ran to
the top of the stairs.

Floppy was scratching at a small
door. Gran slowly turned the
handle.

They saw a small dusty room.

"Come on, Floppy," said Biff.

"Let's have a look around."

Something went flapping across
the room.

"What's that?" said Biff.

Chip pointed. "It's an owl," he whispered. "It must be the face I saw at the window."

"Poor thing! It must have come
down the chimney," said Gran. She
picked it up very gently.

Gran took the owl over to the
window and opened it. The owl
blinked its big round eyes.

"Go on, owl," said
Kipper. "Fly away!"
The owl flapped
its wings and flew
up into the sky.

91

Kipper watched the owl fly away.
"It must be horrible to be trapped,"
he said.

"It is, Kipper," said Gran. "It is!"

Talk about the story

Why did Chip think he had seen a face at the window?

Why did Gran call to the children for help?

Why did Gran keep the gate open with the chest?

What would you do if you found a trapped animal?

Rhyming pairs

Find the four pairs of things that rhyme.
Which is the odd pair out?

Tips for Reading Together

Children learn best when reading is fun.

- Talk about the title and the picture on the cover.
- Discuss what you think the story might be about.
- Read the story together, inviting your child to read as much of it as they can.
- Give lots of praise as your child reads, and help them when necessary.
- If they get stuck, try reading the first sound of the word, or break the word into chunks, or read the whole sentence again. Focus on the meaning.
- Re-read the story later, encouraging your child to read as much of it as they can.

Children enjoy re-reading stories and this helps to build their confidence.

After you have read the story, find the letter shapes in the pictures that spell out the word SNOWBALL.

This book includes these useful common words:
thought   pull(ed)   fast(er)   must   suddenly

For more hints and tips on helping your child become a successful and enthusiastic reader look at our website www.oxfordowl.co.uk.

Husky Adventure

Written by Roderick Hunt
Illustrated by Alex Brychta

OXFORD
UNIVERSITY PRESS

It had been snowing. Kipper
wanted Floppy to pull his sled.
"Go on, Floppy! Pull!" he called.

Floppy didn't want to pull
the sled. He ran and hid in
Biff's bedroom.

Suddenly, the magic key began
to glow. It took Floppy into
an adventure.

The magic took Floppy to a
dark, cold forest. There was
snow everywhere.

The snow felt cold on Floppy's
paws and a cold wind was blowing.
"Brrrr!" thought Floppy.

Floppy began to walk, but his
paws sank in the deep snow.

He heard a howling sound.

AOOOOOW!

"What is that?" thought Floppy.

Oh no! It was a pack of wolves.
They had red eyes and long white
teeth. They growled at Floppy.

Floppy was scared of the wolves.

He ran through the trees.

Suddenly, Floppy fell down.
He rolled over and over. He went
faster and faster.

Then he hit a tree.
BUMP!

BUMP!

Floppy lay in the snow with his
eyes shut.
A man ran up.

"Quick!" he said. "My boy is sick.
I must get him to hospital. I need
another dog to pull the sled."

The man took Floppy to the sled.

"Oh no!" thought Floppy.

"Another pack of wolves!"

But they were not wolves, they
were husky dogs. The dogs growled.
"Are you the new dog? You look
too floppy to pull a sled," they said.

The man put straps on Floppy.
"You've got to run fast," he said.
"We must get to the hospital."

The biggest dog barked at Floppy. "Just keep up, you floppy dog," he said. "We've got to run fast."

Floppy was cross. "Don't call
me a floppy dog," he said. "I'll
show you!"

The sled went faster and faster.
"Slow down!" panted the husky
dogs. "We can't keep up with you."

At last, they got to the hospital.

"Thank you!" shouted the man.

"You've saved my son."

The husky dogs looked at Floppy.
"Wow! You can run fast!" they
said. "You're not a floppy dog."

"You can stay with us," said
the husky dogs. "We need a dog
like you."

The magic key began to glow.
"Good!" thought Floppy. "I need
a rest."

"Come and pull my sled, Floppy,"
said Kipper.

"Oh no!" thought Floppy.

Think about the story

Why did Floppy go and hide?

Did the Huskies think Floppy would be good at pulling the sled? Why not?

Why couldn't the man take his son to hospital in a car?

Where would you like to go on a magic key adventure?

A maze

Help the dog team to find their way to the hospital.

Read with Biff, Chip and Kipper
The UK's best-selling home reading series

Phonics **First Stories**

Level	Phonics	First Stories
Level 1 Getting ready to read	Kipper's Alphabet I Spy Chip's Letter Sounds Biff's Wonder Words Floppy's Fun Phonics	Get On Floppy Did This! Up You Go Six in a Bed
Level 2 Starting to read	I am Kipper Cat in a Bag The Red Hen The Fizz-Buzz... wait	Funny Fish Silly Races! The Snowman Dad's Birthday
Level 3 Becoming a reader	Such a Fuss Shops The Sing Song The Backpack	Poor Old Rabbit I Can Trick a Tiger Super Dad Floppy and the Bone
Level 4 Developing as a reader	Wet Feet The Moon Jet The Red Coat Quick! Quick!	Missing! The Raft Race Dragon Danger The Spaceship
Level 5 Building confidence in reading	Egg Fried Rice Craig Saves the Day  Seasick Dolphin Rescue	Hungry Floppy Husky Adventure Trapped!	Looking after Gran
Level 6 Reading with confidence	Gran's New Blue Shoes Ice City Save Pudding Wood Uncle Max	Hairy-Scary Monster Mountain Rescue The Lost Voice Secret of the Sands

Phonics stories help children practise their sounds and letters, as they learn to do in school.

First Stories have been specially written to provide practice in reading everyday language.

Read with Biff, Chip and Kipper Collections:

 Up You Go and Other Stories

 Six in a Bed and Other Stories

 Funny Fish and Other Stories

 The Fizz-Buzz and Other Stories

 Floppy and the Bone and Other Stories

 I Can Trick a Tiger and Other Stories

 The Moon Jet and Other Stories

 Dragon Danger and Other Stories

 Husky Adventure and Other Stories

 Looking After Gran and Other Stories

Hairy-Scary Monster and Other Stories

Secret of the Sands and Other Stories

Phonics support

READ WITH Biff, Chip & Kipper

Flashcards are a really fun way to practise phonics and build reading skills. Age 3+

My Phonics Kit is designed to support you and your child as you practise phonics together at home. It includes stickers, workbooks, interactive eBooks, support for parents and more! Age 5+

Read Write Inc. PHONICS

Read Write Inc. Phonics: A range of fun rhyming stories to support decoding skills. Age 4+

Songbirds Phonics: Lively and engaging phonics stories from Children's Laureate, Julia Donaldson. Age 4+

Help your child's reading with essential tips, advice on phonics and free eBooks
www.oxfordowl.co.uk